ABOUT THE AUTHORS

SAUNDRIA KECK

Wife to Lee

Mom to Chad (Candace) and Leeanne (Russell)

Grandmom to Hadley, Analayne, Shepherd, and Leighton

Teacher to many—kids and moms, alike

Daughter of God—most important!

KAY BENSON

Wife to Pete

Mom to Kara and Jolen (Chris)

Grandmom to Colton and Sienna (twins)

Teacher to many—kids and moms, alike

Daughter of God—definitely most important!

Remember, and Don't Forget

BIBLE STORIES FOR MOM AND ME

By Saundria Keck and Kay Benson

Illustrated by Kay Benson

ISBN: 978-0-9882147-1-2
www.passthebreadmom.com

We dedicate this book to our husbands, Lee and Pete, who "blessed" this project and supported us in every possible way. We give thanks to our Heavenly Father who led us on this "journey" and provided us with "heavenly road signs" at every turn.

We praise You, O God!

ACKNOWLEDGEMENTS

*Husbands...who patiently supported us through the writing
of this book including preparing fabulous meals for us.
Children. . .who headed up a great team of encouragers.
Mom to Mom Titus 2 Leaders...who faithfully prayed
us through this project.
Ana Carolina Monnaco...who lended her amazing design skills.
Pam Green...who helped Kay take ideas and turn
them into illustrations.
Mark and Alva Duke and Linda Murphy...who shared with
us beautiful and inspiring places to pray, think, and write.*

Thank you, thank you, thank you!

TABLE OF CONTENTS

INTRODUCTION

Perhaps you're a mom who gives a lot of thought to teaching your children about God and have some idea how to do it. Or perhaps you're a mom who gives teaching about God considerable thought, but you're just not sure where to begin. Then you may be a mom who has never given much thought to any of it. Wherever you are, it a good place to begin.

As moms and grandmoms we have noticed that we tend to be creatures with short memories when it comes to learning and living God's Word. We fail to remember; we often forget. Our purpose in writing this book is to take the words from Deuteronomy 11 to heart so they will help us remember and not forget.

"Place God's words in your heart . . . get them deep inside you . . . teach them to your children . . . talk about them wherever you are . . . sitting at home or walking in the street. . . talk about them when you get up in the morning and when you fall in bed at night. . ." These words will be your life.

Moses spoke these words to the children of Israel. He knew if the parents didn't teach their children God's truths, they would soon forget God and go their own way. So over and over Moses reminded them to remember God's love and what He had done for them. Moses knew that following God was the lifeline for both parents and children. So why this book? It is more than a compilation of Bible stories. It is designed to help young children and moms grow together emotionally and spiritually while they engage in God's truths. As you step into this book, you will notice that the chapters are divided into three distinct sections:

I. The Bible Stories/Illustrations
II. The "For Mom and Me" activities
III. The "Just for Mom"

The Bible stories' section is composed of twenty-five foundational stories every child needs to know. The "For Mom and Me" activities are designed to help the child get the truth of the story into both the head and heart through fun interaction with Mom. And the "Just for Mom" section is structured to take mom deeper into scripture so that the story becomes part of her as well. The more the story gets into the mom, the more the story gets into the child. In addition, a Faciliator's Guide is available for moms who would like to delve deeper into the content of this book in a small group study.

Just as Moses continually reminded the children of Israel of God's story and His truths, as parents we must do the same. These stories need to be shared with your little ones again and again. We have learned from our years of training and experience with young children that repetition is essential to learning. So don't hesitate to read or tell the stories over and over and over.

Your child may say: "Mommy, I already know this story." This does not mean that he or she does not want or need to hear the story again. It merely means that he or she is proud to be able to tell you: "I know this story." This will be a good sign to you that the story is getting into the head and heart. So keep on sharing the stories over and over and over.

Our prayer for you is that God will give you a zeal for sharing His Word in a delightful and loving way with your child. And may you both "remember, and not forget."

CHAPTER ONE

IN THE BEGINNING

"God made the beautiful world."
The story of creation, based on Genesis 1 and 2

In the beginning there was nothing. God decided to make something out of nothing. He began making the world. On the first day God said: "Let there be light," and there was light. He called the light day and the darkness He called night. Evening came, and morning came, and that was the first day. On the second day God made the big, big sky. Evening came and morning came and that was the second day.

On the third day God made water and dry ground. The water He called ocean and the dry ground He called land. Then God saw that the land needed plants, and trees, and flowers. So He made them. Evening came, and morning came, and that was the third day. On the fourth day God looked at the sky. He saw that it needed a sun, a moon, and stars. So He made them. Evening came, and morning came, and that was the fourth day.

On the fifth day God looked at the ocean and decided it needed fish. He looked at the sky and decided it needed birds. So He made them. Evening came, and morning came, and that was the fifth day.

On the sixth day God looked at the land and decided that it needed animals—like elephants, tigers, and lizards. But God knew something was still missing. People were missing. So God made a man and called him Adam, and a woman and called her Eve. Evening came, and morning came, and that was the sixth day.

Then the seventh day came and God rested.

FOR MOM AND ME

WE CAN TALK

Talk with your child about the activities of the day. Help him or her think of specific things (such as ate breakfast, played with a friend, drew a picture). Comment: "Wow, you've really done a lot today. God did a lot when He made the world." Ask your child: "Then what did God do?" (He rested.) Give him or her a gentle hug and say: "Now it's time for you to rest."

WE CAN PLAY

Cover a card table with a blanket that drapes over the sides. Crawl under the table with your child. Take a flashlight with you. Talk about how dark it is. Then let your child turn on the flashlight and talk about how there is light. In our Bible story, God said: "Let there be light," and there was light.

WE CAN DO

Take a walk with your child and look for things God made. You may want to take a basket or small bag for your child to collect nature items like a rock, a flower, or a twig. As you walk talk about things God made.

WE CAN PRAY

"Dear God, Thank You for making a beautiful world. (Encourage your child to name things God made.) Amen."

WE CAN REMEMBER

God made the beautiful world.

JUST FOR MOM

GROW WITH YOUR CHILD

READ

Genesis 1 through 2:1-3

THINK ABOUT

1. What were the "somethings" God made out of "nothing"?

2. As you read the scripture, underline the words: "It was good." Why do you think God continually noted: "It was good"?

3. According to the scripture in whose image were you created?

4. How does this TRUTH make you feel (confused, scared, comforted, skeptical, amazed)? Why?

PRAY

Pray thanking God for His good creations including yourself and your family. (You may want to start a gratitude journal.)

REMEMBER

God created man in his own image, in the image of God he created him; male and female he created them. Genesis 1:27 (NIV)

CHAPTER TWO

TWO BY TWO

"God takes care of us."
The story of Noah, based on Genesis 6-9

Noah lived many years ago. He loved God, walked with God, talked with God, and listened to God. But God was sad because the people on earth did not love Him—except for Noah.

One day God talked to Noah and said: "Noah, build an ark (big boat) because I'm going to send rain, lots and lots of rain. The rain will cover the whole earth." So Noah listened to God and did just what He said. Noah started building the ark. He sawed—swish, swish, swish. He hammered—tap, tap, tap. He worked and worked to build the ark just the way God told him to. Then it was time to go inside.

Noah gathered his wife, his three sons and their wives. Then he gathered the animals—two cows, two ducks, two zebras, two lady bugs—two of every kind of animal. Then God said: "It's time. Come in." So Noah and his wife, his three sons and their wives, and all the animals, two by two, entered the ark. Then they heard a loud sound. God had shut the door (boom!) to keep them safe.

The rain came. It rained and rained and rained—water everywhere. But Noah and his family and all the animals were safe. Then one day God said to Noah: "Noah, the rain is over. The land is dry and it is safe to go outside." So Noah and his wife, his three sons and their wives, and all the animals, two by two, stepped onto dry land. Then God said: "Look into the sky. See the rainbow?" The rainbow was God's way of letting Noah know that it would never rain that much again.

FOR MOM AND ME

WE CAN TALK

Say to your child: "We're going to sing a song about Noah." To the tune "Old McDonald" sing these words: " Old man Noah had an ark, eei-eei-o. And on his ark, he had a cow, eei-eei-o. With a moo-moo here and a moo-moo there, here a moo, there a moo, everywhere a moo-moo. Old man Noah had an ark, eei-eei-o." Ask your child to choose other animals to include in the song.

WE CAN PLAY

Make play dough with your child using the recipe below:

1 cup flour	1 teaspoon oil
1 cup warm water	1/4 cup salt
2 teaspoons cream of tartar	food coloring (one color)

Mix all ingredients, adding food coloring last. Stir over medium heat until smooth. Remove from pan and knead until blended. Place in a plastic bag or airtight container when cooled. Provide small vinyl animals for your child to use with the play dough.

WE CAN DO

Gather your family around a table free from distraction. Let your children bring several stuffed animals. Discuss what it might have been like for Noah and his family.

WE CAN PRAY

"Dear God, thank You for taking care of us. Amen."

WE CAN REMEMBER

God takes care of me.

JUST FOR MOM

GROW WITH YOUR CHILD

READ

Genesis 6:1-8

THINK ABOUT

1. What grieved the Lord's heart?

2. What was different about Noah?

3. Who benefited from Noah's relationship with God? Why?

4. How did God "mark" His promise with Noah? Do you think it is important to "mark" promises?

PRAY

Pray to hear God's voice and the strength and to do what He says.

REMEMBER

The Lord was grieved that he made man on the earth, and his heart was filled with pain. Genesis 6:6 (NIV)

CHAPTER THREE

GOD PROMISES A BIG, BIG FAMILY

"God keeps His promises."
The story of Abraham, Sarah, and Isaac, based on Genesis 15; 21:1-7

A braham lived many, many years ago. He wanted a family but he was an old man, too old to have babies. Abraham and God talked about the problem. God said: "Don't be afraid to talk to me, Abraham. I can handle your problem." Then Abraham said: "I have waited all my life to have children—to have a family. God answered: "Come outside with me, Abraham. They walked outside even though it was night. God said: "Look up, Abraham. What do you see?" Abraham did what God said and looked up into the nighttime sky. He could see stars, hundred of stars, thousands of stars—so many stars he could not even begin to count them. God told Abraham that he would have a family—children, grandchildren, great grandchildren—a really big family. So many he could not count them, just like the stars.

Abraham looked at his hair; it was white. He looked at his skin; it was wrinkled. He looked at his shoulders; they were stooped. He thought about how he felt. He was tired. Then Abraham began to think about his wife, Sarah. She was old, too. She was much too old to have a baby. Abraham had a decision to make. Was he going to believe God or not? Even though God's promise seemed impossible, Abraham believed God. He believed he would have big family.

A year later, Abraham and his wife, Sarah, had a son and they named him Isaac. When Isaac grew up, he had children. And when his children's children grew up, they had children. Soon there were more children than they could count—a really big family—just like the stars. Just like God promised!

FOR MOM AND ME

WE CAN TALK

Turn out the lights. Go to a window and look out at the nighttime sky. Ask your child if he or she can count all the stars they see.

Then encourage your child to help you name and count the members of your extended family. Comment: "God promised Abraham a big family just like the stars in the sky."

WE CAN PLAY

Provide black construction paper and yellow or white chalk (or crayon). Encourage your child to draw as many stars as he or she can on the "nighttime sky." You might say: "This reminds me of the story of Abraham."

WE CAN DO

As a family go to a planetarium if there is one near you. If not, take a drive into the country where there are no city lights. As you gaze at the stars, talk about the time God took Abraham outside and showed him all the stars.

WE CAN PRAY

"Dear God, thank You for doing what You say You will do. Amen."

WE CAN REMEMBER

God will do what He says He will do.

JUST FOR MOM

GROW WITH YOUR CHILD

READ

Genesis 15; 21:1-7

THINK ABOUT

1. What was Abraham's problem?

2. How did God handle Abraham's problem?

3. Why was God's solution difficult for Abraham to believe?

4. How did Abraham eventually respond to God's promise and why?

PRAY

Pray that God will help you believe even when His ways seem impossible.

REMEMBER

He [God] took him outside and said, "Look up to the heavens and count the stars—if indeed you can count them." Then he said to him [Abraham], "So shall your offspring be." Abram [Abraham] believed the Lord, and he [God] credited it to him as righteousness. Genesis 15:5-6 (NIV)

CHAPTER FOUR

A HIDDEN BABY

"People in families need to take care of each other."
The story of Baby Moses, based on Exodus 2:1-10; Numbers 26:59

I n the country of Egypt there lived a mean king called Pharaoh. All the people were afraid of him.

There was a family who had a new baby boy. They did not want the king to hurt their baby. So the mama kept him hidden inside their house until he grew too big to hide. Then the baby's mama made a little basket to put the baby in. She made the basket out of reeds and covered it with sticky stuff called tar.

The mama wrapped her baby in a soft blanket and laid him gently in the basket. Then the mama and the baby's big sister, Miriam, took him down to the edge of the Nile River where there was lots of tall grass. They carefully placed the little basket along the edge of the river. Miriam hid in the tall grass and watched over her baby brother.

Along came the king's daughter, the princess, with her helpers. She was coming to the river to take a bath. One of the helpers saw the little basket floating in the water. The helper took it and gave it to the princess. She looked inside and saw the soft blanket and heard the baby cry. She felt sorry for him. Then Miriam ran to the princess and asked: "Do you want me to find someone to take care of the baby?"

 "Yes," said the princess. Miriam ran home to get their mama and brought her back. The princess asked the mama to care for the baby and she did. The princess named the baby Moses because she pulled him out of the water.

FOR MOM AND ME

WE CAN TALK

Ask your child: "What did mommy do to take care of you (sister, brother) today?" You might also want to ask: "Did you do something to take care of somebody in our family today?"

WE CAN PLAY

Gather a laundry basket, a doll (or stuffed animal), and a baby blanket. Encourage your to child to wrap up the "baby" and place him carefully in the basket. Give your child the opportunity to act out the story.

WE CAN DO

Tell your child you are going to take a "short" rest. Ask your child: "What could you do to help me rest?" Come up with ideas together. You might suggest things like: taking off your shoes, helping put your feet up on the sofa, placing a pillow under your head and bringing you a magazine or favorite book. Encourage your child to play quietly nearby while you take a "short" rest. At the end of the rest, say: "People in families take care of each other. Thank you for taking care of me."

WE CAN PRAY

"Dear God, thank You for giving us families who take care of us. Amen."

WE CAN REMEMBER

God made my family to take care of me.

JUST FOR MOM

GROW WITH YOUR CHILD

READ

Exodus 1:22 through 2:10

THINK ABOUT

1. Why were the Hebrew families afraid of Pharaoh?

2. What did Moses' mother do to protect him?

3. How do you think Moses' mother felt when Miriam informed her that the princess had discovered Baby Moses?

4. Scripture teaches that Moses became a great leader of the Hebrew people. How do you think Moses' mother influenced him in the brief time she had with him?

PRAY

Pray asking God to help you make the most of the time you have with your child (children).

REMEMBER

Then his sister asked Pharaoh's daughter, "Shall I go and get one of the Hebrew women to nurse the baby for you?" "Yes, go," she answered. And the girl went and got the baby's mother. Exodus 2:7-8 (NIV)

CHAPTER FIVE

THE WALLS CAME TUMBLING DOWN

"God is strong and mighty."
The story of Joshua and the Walls of Jericho, based on Joshua 5 and 6

There once was a soldier named Joshua who was a leader of a large army of God's people. Long ago God had promised his people a land green with grass for their sheep, rich with good food to eat, and enough milk and honey for all to enjoy. But there was a problem. Jericho.

They had to take over the city of Jericho to get to the land God promised them. Joshua and his army usually fought with spears and swords, but this time God had a different plan. God told them to march around Jericho every day for six days. They were not to fight, not even to speak a word. On the seventh day the army was to march around the city seven times while seven priests blew their horns.

They marched around Jericho on the first day, then on the second, the third, the fourth, the fifth, and the sixth day. But nothing happened. On the seventh day, Joshua and his army marched around Jericho seven times—one, two, three, four, five, six, seven. Then seven priests blew their trumpets and Joshua yelled: "Shout!" All the soldiers shouted as loudly as they could.

All were amazed for the walls of Jericho came tumbling down. God's people entered the land God promised them. They enjoyed green pastures for their sheep, good food for their tables, and milk and honey for all. God did just what He said. He took care of His people.

FOR MOM AND ME

WE CAN TALK

Say to your child: "Let's sing a song about Joshua." To the tune of the song "The Ants Go Marching Round and Round," sing these words: "Joshua's men went marching round the walls, the walls. Joshua's men went marching round the walls, the walls. Joshua's men went marching round, they blew their horns, they heard the sound. And the walls came tumbling down, down, down, down, down."

WE CAN PLAY

Use wooden blocks to construct the "walls of Jericho." Pretend to blow a horn. Shout and allow your child to knock the walls down. Your child will enjoy doing this over and over.

WE CAN DO

Take a field trip to an area with large, well-constructed buildings. Talk about how strong and mighty God would have to be to knock down the buildings with the blast of a horn and a loud shout. Take photos of the buildings and use the photos to illustrate a book your child dictates to you when you return home.

WE CAN PRAY

"Dear God, thank You for being strong and mighty. Amen."

WE CAN REMEMBER

God is strong and mighty.

JUST FOR MOM

GROW WITH YOUR CHILD

READ

Joshua 6:1-20

THINK ABOUT

1. What was Joshua's problem?

2. What was God's solution?

3. Why do you think Joshua embraced such an unusual solution to the problem?

4. How would you describe Joshua's relationship with God?

PRAY

Pray that God would help you experience His strength and might today.

REMEMBER

Then the Lord said to Joshua, "See, I have delivered Jericho into your hands. . ." Joshua 6:2 (NIV)

CHAPTER SIX

A NEW KING

"God looks at the heart."
The story of David, based on 1 Samuel 16:1-13

S amuel was one of God's special helpers. God told him to go to Bethlehem to find a man named Jesse, who had eight sons. One of the sons would become the new king.

When Samuel arrived in Bethlehem, he met Jesse and seven of his sons. As soon as Samuel saw the son named Eliab, he thought: "This has to be the one God wants to be king. He is tall and handsome and looks like a king." But God said: "No, this is not the one. People look at the face, but I look at the heart."

Next Samuel met the son named Abinadab. He walked in front of Samuel, but Samuel knew that Abinadab was not God's choice either.

Then Jesse brought in Shammah. God again said: "No, it's not this one either." Soon Jesse had presented seven of his sons to Samuel. Samuel said: "God has not chosen any of these sons." Finally Samuel asked Jesse: "Do you have any other sons?" Jesse said: "Yes, I have one more son, but he's the youngest. He's out in the field taking care of the sheep."

Samuel told Jesse to go get him. So Jesse sent for his son, David. When David walked in, Samuel knew that he was the man who would someday become king. He said: "This is the one!" Samuel learned that God looks at the heart, not the face.

FOR MOM AND ME

WE CAN TALK

Hold a mirror where your child can see his or her reflection. Ask: "What do you see?" Give your child the opportunity to describe what he or she sees (nose, mouth, eyes). Then say: "I see your eyes, nose, and mouth, but I also see your kindness to your grandmother, your love for your sister, and your funny laugh." Finally ask: "What do you think God sees when He looks at you and at me?"

WE CAN PLAY

Cut a crown out of newspaper or construction paper. Provide scissors, glue, markers, and sparkles. Let your child decorate the crown. Then put it on his or her head. Comment: "David became king because God looked at his kind heart."

WE CAN DO

During the week, make an intentional effort of affirming attributes and character traits you notice in your child rather than outward appearance.

WE CAN PRAY

"Dear God, thank You for looking inside and outside of me. Amen."

WE CAN REMEMBER

Who I am on the inside is more important than how I look on the outside.

JUST FOR MOM

GROW WITH YOUR CHILD

READ

1 Samuel 16:1-13

THINK ABOUT

1. Why was Samuel looking to anoint a new king?

2. If Samuel had been selecting the new king apart from God's direction, what kind of man would he have chosen?

3. How does God look at a person? How do we tend to look at a person?

4. Will this scripture passage affect how you look at yourself in the future? Your husband? Your children? Others? Journal your thoughts.

PRAY

Ask God to help you be more careful to look at a person's heart rather his or her face (status, wealth, etc).

REMEMBER

"The Lord does not look at the things man looks at. Man looks at the outward appearance, but the Lord looks at the heart."
1 Samuel 16:7b (NIV)

CHAPTER SEVEN

FRIENDS FOREVER

"It is important to do what you say you will do."
The story of David and Jonathan, based on 1 Samuel 16:14-23; 18:1-5

In the country of Israel there lived a mighty king named Saul. He often became sad and weary and had trouble falling asleep. King Saul's servants said: "We see that you are very sad. Perhaps the soothing music of a harp might help you rest." So King Saul told his servants: "Quick! Go find someone to play the harp and bring him to me."

The servants hurried off to Bethlehem where they found a young man named David who could play the harp. So David went to live in the palace of King Saul and played the harp to help the king rest. David was also a brave warrior.

While David was living in the palace, he became good friends with King Saul's son, Jonathan, who was also a brave soldier. Jonathan loved David like a brother.

One day Jonathan said to David: "I'm glad we're friends. I will help you whenever you need help." Then David said: "I will help you, too." So Jonathan gave David his special coat as a reminder of his promise. He also gave him his armor, his sword, his bow, and his belt.

David knew Jonathan would keep his promise. He knew he would do what he said he would do. David and Jonathan loved each other like brothers and wanted to be friends as long as they lived.

FOR MOM AND ME

WE CAN TALK

Think back through the activities of the day with your child. Encourage your child to recall a time when he or she did what you asked (brushed teeth, put away a toy, brought a diaper for the baby, put on pajamas). Affirm by saying something like: "That's good. It is important to do what you say you will do."

WE CAN PLAY

Make a simple pictorial chore chart (pictures from magazines, simple line drawings, etc.) highlighting three chores you would like for your child to do each day. Sit down with your child and explain the chart. Say something like: "It is going to be your responsibility to do these three chores each day. I will help you remember." When your child completes each chore, give him or her sticker or star to place on the chart and say: "Great. You did what you said you would do."

WE CAN DO

As a mom think of three things you say you will do with or for your child and follow through. When you do, remind your child that you did what you said you would do. You might say: "See. I did what I said I would do." (Example: After your nap, we will go outside to play.)

WE CAN PRAY

"Dear God, help me remember to do what I say I will do. Amen."

WE CAN REMEMBER

God wants me to do what I say I will do.

JUST FOR MOM

GROW WITH YOUR CHILD

READ

1 Samuel 16:14-23; 18:1-5; 20:23b

THINK ABOUT

1. How did David and Jonathan become friends?

2. In *The Message* by Eugene Peterson he states that Jonathan "would be David's number-one advocate and friend." What does it mean to be someone's "number-one advocate and friend"?

3. What part does trustworthiness play in true friendship?

4. Journal about the importance of being trustworthy (doing what you say you will do) in a current relationship with someone you truly care about.

PRAY

Ask God to show you where you need to be more trustworthy in the relationships closest to you.

REMEMBER

". . . remember, the Lord is witness between you and me forever."
1 Samuel 20:23b (NIV)

CHAPTER EIGHT

A LITTLE GIRL HELPS

"It's important to do things God's way."
The story of Naaman, based on 2 Kings 5

Naaman was a very important man. He told people what to do, and they listened to him. But he had a problem. He had a terrible skin disease. He wanted to get well, but he didn't know how. No one could help him--that is until a little girl came along.

The little girl helped Naaman's wife around the house. She swept floors, baked bread, and washed dishes. She wanted to help with Naaman's problem. She said to Naaman's wife: "I know a special man of God who lives in Israel. He can help Naaman get well."

So Naaman went to Israel. First he went to the king, but the king said he could not make Naaman well. Then Elisha, the special man of God, heard about Naaman and said: "Send Naaman to me. He will learn that my God can help."

So Naaman went to Elisha's house. Elisha's servant told him: "Go to the River Jordan and dip in the water seven times. Then your skin will be healed and you will be as good as new."

Naaman was angry. He did not want to dip in a dirty old river seven times. But his servants said: "Naaman, you want to get well, don't you? Then dip in the river like Elisha said." So he did! He got in the Jordan River. He went down one time, then two, then three, then four, then five, then six, then seven. He looked at his skin. He could hardly believe his eyes. His skin was clean—as soft as a baby—no more disease. Naaman was glad he listened and did what God said.

FOR MOM AND ME

WE CAN TALK

Draw a simple face on your index finger. Pretend the finger is Naaman. Together with your child count to seven as you pretend to dip Naaman in the water of the Jordan River.

WE CAN PLAY

Take a bar of white soap, and with a red washable marker, draw a simple face on the soap. Then add red dots all over the surface. Fill a sink or pan with water. Give your child time to play with the bar of soap until all the spots wash off.

WE CAN DO

With your child think of a neighbor, family member, or church friend who is sick. Write his or her name on a note card and attach it to your refrigerator. Set aside a special time to pray with your child for that person each day.

WE CAN PRAY

"Dear God, teach me to do things Your way. Amen."

WE CAN REMEMBER

I can do things God's way.

JUST FOR MOM

GROW WITH YOUR CHILD

READ

2 Kings 5

THINK ABOUT

1. Look back at Naaman's situation. What was his real problem?

2. How did God deal with Naaman's problem? Write your answer below.

3. What was Naaman's response to Elisha's request?

4. What did Naaman learn from his experience? Write your answer in the space below.

PRAY

Pray about a current problem you're facing. Write your prayer.

REMEMBER

So he went down and dipped himself in the Jordan seven times, as the man of God had told him, and his flesh was restored and became clean like that of a young boy. 2 Kings 5:14 (NIV)

CHAPTER NINE

A SPECIAL ROOM FOR A SPECIAL GUEST

"We can be kind to people who visit us."
The story of Elisha, based on 2 Kings 4:8-11

One day Elisha, a man of God, was in the town of Shunem. While he was there, he met a woman who was very rich. She invited Elisha to her house for dinner. Elisha enjoyed visiting in her home and eating dinner there. So every time he was in Shunem, he went to the home of the woman and her husband and enjoyed a meal with them.

After awhile the woman said to her husband: "You know how happy we are when Elisha comes to visit? We need a place for him to stay. Could we build a room for him?"

They agreed they would build a small room on the roof of their house. They could put a bed in the room. They could also put a table and chair. And of course they would put an oil lamp so Elisha could have light at night. Then whenever Elisha was in Shunem, he would have a cozy and quiet place to stay.

Later Elisha came to visit the woman and her husband again. He was glad to have a room on the roof of their house. He walked up the stairs to the roof and went into his special room. There he found a bed, a table, a chair, and an oil lamp to give him light at night. He lay down on the bed and went to sleep.

FOR MOM AND ME

WE CAN TALK
Ask your child to help you recall things you do to get ready for people (grandparents, aunts/uncles, friends) who come to visit you.

WE CAN PLAY
Using any kind of blocks (or clean empty milk cartons), help your child build a house with a flat roof. Then add a room on the roof. Ask your child to list things he or she would put in the room to help visitors enjoy coming to your house.

WE CAN DO
Make a hospitality basket with your child. Gather a basket, soap, lotion, toothpaste, toothbrush, shampoo, tissues, bottle of water, alarm clock, and a magazine. Tie an attractive ribbon around the basket so it is ready when guests are expected. While putting together the basket, talk with your child about the woman and her husband who built a room for Elisha.

WE CAN PRAY
"Dear God, help our family be kind to people who come to visit. Amen."

WE CAN REMEMBER
I can be kind to visitors.

JUST FOR MOM

GROW WITH YOUR CHILD

READ

2 Kings 4:8-13

THINK ABOUT

1. How and why did the Shunammite woman and her husband show kindness to Elisha?

2. Write about a time you were shown hospitality and how it made you feel?

3. How do you show kindness to visitors? Why?

4. List five ways you can show hospitality without spending money.

PRAY

Ask God to show you how to offer simple kindness to people who visit your home.

REMEMBER

So whenever he [Elisha] came by, he stopped there to eat.
2 Kings 4:8 (NIV)

CHAPTER TEN

A SURPRISE IN THE TEMPLE

"God wants us to do what the Bible says."
The story of young King Josiah, based on 2 Kings 22 through 23:1-3

J osiah was eight years old when he became king. Even as a little boy, Josiah did what God wanted him to do.

When Josiah grew to be a man, he noticed that the temple (church building) needed to be repaired. It was a mess. So he called in carpenters, construction workers, and masons. The carpenters and construction workers used hammers, saws, and nails. The masons used bricks, stones, and mortar. They worked together to repair the temple.

While the temple was being repaired, a helper named Hilkiah found something special. It was a Bible scroll. The words in the Bible scroll told the people what God wanted them to do. Some helpers took the Bible scroll to King Josiah. When he read the words of God, he was sad because the people were not doing what God wanted them to do.

King Josiah wanted all the people of Judah to hear these important words. He told the people to come to the temple and they all came. King Josiah read the important words from the Bible scroll. When they heard the words, they promised to do what God wanted them to do. And God was pleased with King Josiah.

FOR MOM AND ME

WE CAN TALK

Play a game called "Let's Pretend."

- Pretend to be a temple helper. Which job would you like to do?
- Pretend to be Hilkiah. What did Hilkiah find? How do you think he felt?
- Pretend to be King Josiah. What did he tell the people? Why do you think God was pleased with King Josiah?

WE CAN PLAY

Play a game of "Hide and Find." Gather several Bibles or make scrolls by rolling sheets of paper from opposite ends to the middle. Hide the Bibles or scrolls in various places in the room. Then encourage your child to "find" them. Say something like: "The Bible has important words. We need to do what they say."

WE CAN DO

If your child does not have his or her own Bible, this would be good time to get one. Go to a bookstore or online with your child and choose a children's Bible (not a Bible story book) such as the *Read to Me Bible for Kids*, published by Holman. Keep the Bible where it is readily available to your child.

WE CAN PRAY

"Dear God, thank You for the Bible. Help me do what it says. Amen."

WE CAN REMEMBER

Do what the Bible says.

JUST FOR MOM

GROW WITH YOUR CHILD

READ

2 Kings 22; 23:1-3

THINK ABOUT

1. What led the workers to discover the scroll in the Temple?

2. Why was the scroll important?

3. Why was Josiah so dismayed when he heard what was written on the scroll?

4. What did Josiah lead the people to do in response to the reading of the scroll? What is God leading you to do in response to reading 2 Kings 22 and 23:1-3?

PRAY

Ask God to lead you to know and do what the Bible says.

REMEMBER

He did what was right in the eyes of the Lord . . . not turning aside to the right or to the left. 2 Kings 22:2 (NIV)

CHAPTER ELEVEN

A NIGHT TO REMEMBER

"Jesus was a very special baby."
The story of Jesus' birth, based on Matthew 1:18-24; Luke 2:1-20

J oseph and Mary traveled to the city of Bethlehem. It was a long day's journey. They got there late in the evening and they were tired. They needed a place to sleep, but all the rooms were full.

A kind inn keeper said: "You can come sleep in my stable with my animals. I have donkeys, and cows, and sheep sleeping there, but there is plenty of room for you as well."

Joseph and Mary were happy to have even a stable to sleep in. During the night, something very special happened—Mary had a baby boy and they named Him Jesus. They wrapped Him in soft blankets and laid Him in a manger.

That same night in the fields near Bethlehem, shepherds were taking care of their sheep. All at once an angel appeared to them and they were frightened. But the angel said: "Don't be afraid. I have good news for you. A very special baby named Jesus was born tonight in the city of Bethlehem. Go see Him." Then the angel added: "You will know Him because you will find Him wrapped in soft baby blankets lying in a manger."

The shepherds hurried off to Bethlehem to find the baby Jesus. They found Joseph and Mary. Then they saw the baby, wrapped in blankets, lying in the manger just as the angel had said.

FOR MOM AND ME

WE CAN TALK

Encourage your child to pretend he or she is:

Holding the baby

Rocking the baby

Wrapping the baby in a blanket

Patting the baby's back

Kissing the baby good night

WE CAN PLAY

Provide a cardboard box and some newspaper. Show your child how to tear the paper into strips to look like hay. Let your child fill the box with newspaper strips. Comment: "This is kind of like the manger where Mary and Joseph laid Baby Jesus."

WE CAN DO

Look through magazines for pictures of babies. Talk to your child about how each baby is different. Then say: "All babies are special, but Jesus was the most special baby."

WE CAN PRAY

"Dear God, thank You for Baby Jesus. Amen."

WE CAN REMEMBER

Jesus was a very special baby.

JUST FOR MOM

GROW WITH YOUR CHILD

READ

Matthew 1:18-24; Luke 2:1-20

THINK ABOUT

1. How was the conception of Jesus like no other?

2. Why do you think God chose a stable as the place of Jesus' birth?

3. How did God choose to announce Jesus' birth and to whom? Why?

4. Why was Jesus the most special baby ever born?

PRAY

Ask God to make the significance of Jesus' birth more real to you.

REMEMBER

Today in the town of David a Savior has been born to you; he is Christ the Lord. Luke 2:11 (NIV)

CHAPTER TWELVE

WAITING ON JESUS

"Thank God for Jesus."
The story of Simeon and Anna, based on Luke 2:21-40

For many, many years God's people had been waiting for Jesus to be born. They had prayed and waited, prayed and waited, and prayed and waited some more. Finally, Jesus had been born in Bethlehem just as God promised.

When Jesus was only eight days old, his mother, Mary, and father, Joseph, took Him to the temple (church). While they were there, they met a man named Simeon. He was an old man who loved God very much. He had been waiting a long, long time to see Jesus.

When Simeon saw the baby Jesus, he took Him in his arms and said: "Thank You, God, for letting me see this baby." Simeon knew in his heart he had seen the special baby God had promised to send.

At the same time there was a woman at the temple named Anna. She also was old and loved God very much and had been waiting a long time to see Jesus. Anna lived at the temple night and day and spent all her time praying to God. When she saw Mary, Joseph and the baby Jesus, she immediately came over to them. She looked up and said: "Thank You, God, for this special baby." She then turned around and told all who would listen: "Look! This is Jesus—the One we've been waiting for."

FOR MOM AND ME

WE CAN TALK

Show a photo of your child as a baby. Talk about how small he or she was. Notice how much hair the baby had. Then ask your child: "Who was holding you?" Comment: "Simeon and Anna held Jesus when He was a baby like you."

WE CAN PLAY

Gather a sheet of white paper and some crayons. Fold the paper in half to make a card. Write on the front: "Thank You, God, for Jesus." Then encourage your child to decorate the card. Display it where your child and others can see it.

WE CAN DO

Encourage your child to add, "Thank You, God, for Jesus," to his or her prayers each night. Teaching by example, let your child hear you thank God for Jesus as well.

WE CAN PRAY

"Dear God, thank You for Jesus. Amen."

WE CAN REMEMBER

Thank God for Jesus.

JUST FOR MOM

GROW WITH YOUR CHILD

READ

Luke 2:21-40

THINK ABOUT

1. For what had God's people been praying and waiting?

2. Why did Mary and Joseph take Jesus to the temple?

3. Why do you think Simeon and Anna recognized Jesus immediately?

4. Why was Jesus the One they had been waiting for?

PRAY

Pray, thanking God for Jesus, the Giver of your salvation.

REMEMBER

For my eyes have seen your salvation. Luke 2:30 (NIV)

CHAPTER THIRTEEN

GIFTS FOR THE BABY

"I can give gifts."
The story of the Wise Men, based on Matthew 2:1-12

There were wise men who lived far, far away in the east. They were called Magi because they were very smart men. When they saw a special star in the sky, they knew it was a sign that Jesus had been born. So they prepared to go on a journey to find Him. They wanted to give Him gifts. Along with their food, water, and clothes, they packed gold, frankincense, and myrrh to give to Jesus. They knew it was going to be a long, long trip for them and their camels.

The wise men followed the bright star in the sky night after night until they came to Jerusalem. There they met King Herod who had heard about their search for the baby Jesus. The king said: "Go to Bethlehem and find the baby so I can worship Him, too." But the king didn't really want to worship the baby; he was jealous of Him.

The wise men started on their journey once again. They followed the bright star in the sky. The star stopped over the place where Jesus was. The wise men were overjoyed when the star stopped. They were so excited to see Jesus and give the gifts they had brought. They went into the house where Jesus was with his mother, Mary. They fell on their knees and thanked God for Jesus. Out of their bags they brought treasures of gold, frankincense, and myrrh—special gifts for a special baby.

In a dream the wise men were told not to return to King Herod. So they traveled home another way. They were glad they could give their gifts to Jesus.

FOR MOM AND ME

WE CAN TALK

Ask your child: "If you could give a gift to anyone in the whole wide world, who would it be? And what would you give?" Enjoy discussing who you would give a gift to and what it would be as well.

WE CAN PLAY

Provide boxes (several sizes), wrapping paper, ribbon, tape, and child-sized scissors. Engage your child in wrapping the boxes as he or she desires. Provide help as needed. Pretend to give gifts to people your child loves. Recall the story of the wise men giving gifts to Jesus.

WE CAN DO

Weave this Bible verse into your conversation with your child over the next week: "You're far happier giving than getting" (Acts 20:35, The Message). See where the conversation goes.

WE CAN PRAY

"Dear God, help me be a happy giver. Amen."

WE CAN REMEMBER

Wise Men gave gifts to Jesus.

JUST FOR MOM

GROW WITH YOUR CHILD

READ

Matthew 2:1-12

THINK ABOUT

1. What signaled the birth of Jesus to the Wise Men?

2. How was the Wise Men's motive for finding Jesus different from King Herod's?

3. Why did the Wise Men bring highly treasured gifts to Jesus?

4. If you could give Jesus a gift today, what would you give? Why?

PRAY

Ask God to give you a more generous heart toward Him.

REMEMBER

...they bowed down and worshiped him. Then they opened their treasures and presented him with gifts... Matthew 2:11b (NIV)

CHAPTER FOURTEEN

CALLED BY NAME

"We can be helpers."
The story of Jesus choosing helpers, based on Matthew 4:18-22; Mark 1:14-20

One day Jesus was walking on the beach by the Sea of Galilee. As Jesus was walking along, he saw two brothers, one named Peter and one named Andrew. The brothers were fishing with nets. Fishing was their work.

Jesus asked the brothers to help him with some special work. Jesus meant he wanted them, Peter and Andrew, to help him tell people the good news that God loved them. The brothers listened, put down their nets, and did just what Jesus asked. They followed Him.

Jesus, Peter and Andrew walked a little further down the beach where they saw two more brothers. They were fishermen, too. Their names were James and John. They were in a boat with their father, Zebedee. They were getting their nets ready to fish. Fishing was their work also.

Jesus asked James and John to be his helpers, too. The brothers listened, dropped their nets, and did just what Jesus asked. Jesus, Andrew, Peter, James, and John got to work telling people about God.

FOR MOM AND ME

WE CAN TALK

Before telling the story, encourage your child to line up five favorite stuffed animals at the end of the bed. Following the story, ask your child to choose two of the animals to be helpers. Ask: "Why did you choose these two to be your helpers?" Give your child time to respond and then ask: "Why do you think Jesus chose Peter, Andrew, James and John to be his helpers?"

WE CAN PLAY

Provide toy plastic boats, fish, and pretend fish nets (such as a mesh produce bags) to use in the bathtub or as water play. As your child plays with the toys in the water, ask him or her: "Can you catch fish in your net?" Then comment: "That reminds me of some fishermen in the Bible. Can you remember their names? (Give your child time to think and respond: Peter, Andrew, James and John.). Jesus chose Peter, Andrew, James, and John to be his helpers."

WE CAN DO

Reinforce the concept and vocabulary of this story by saying something like: "I choose you to help me set the table (make the bed, water the flowers, and so forth) just like Jesus chose friends to help him."

WE CAN PRAY

"Dear God, thank you for loving me. Thank You that I can be Jesus' helper. Amen."

WE CAN REMEMBER

Jesus chooses helpers.

JUST FOR MOM

GROW WITH YOUR CHILD

READ

Matthew 4:18-22; Mark 1:14-20

THINK ABOUT

1. What were Peter, Andrew, James and John doing when they encountered Jesus by the Sea of Galilee?

2. How did Jesus use what the fishermen were doing to communicate what He was calling them to do?

3. What do you think Jesus meant when he said: "I will make you fishers of men"?

4. Journal about how Jesus might use your everyday experiences to help others learn about Him.

PRAY

Ask God to help you be a willing follower of Jesus.

REMEMBER

"Come, follow me," Jesus said, "and I will make you fishers of men." Mark 1:17 (NIV)

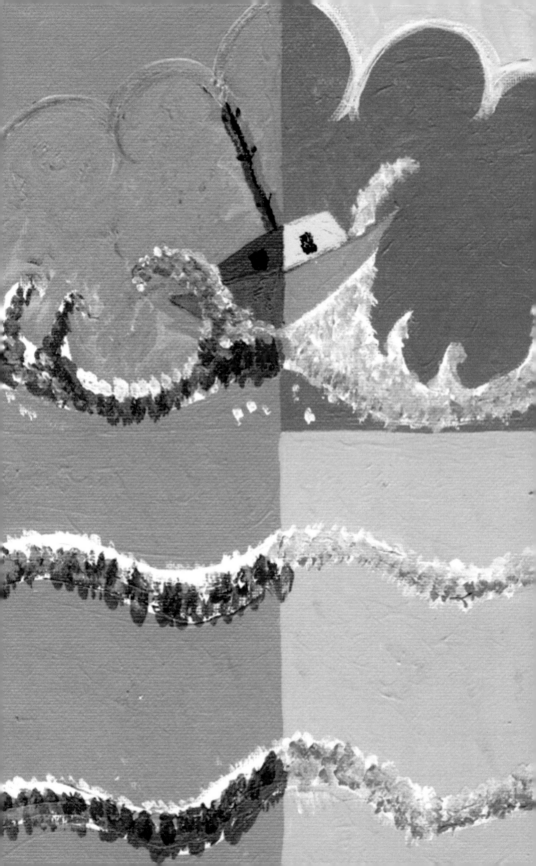

CHAPTER FIFTEEN

WHEN JESUS SAID "SHHH"

"Jesus wants us to trust Him when we are afraid."
The story of Jesus and the storm, based on Matthew 8:23-27; Mark 4:35-41; Luke 8:22-25

One evening Jesus said to His friends: "Let's go to the other side of the Sea of Galilee." They climbed into a boat and started across the water.

At first everything was quiet. The sky was clear and the water was smooth. But while they were sailing across the sea, the sky suddenly got dark, the wind began to blow, and the waves swelled so high the water splashed into the boat. Jesus' friends were afraid.

Jesus, with His head on a pillow, was asleep near the back of the boat. He wasn't afraid at all. Jesus' friends woke Him and said: "Jesus, Jesus, wake up! This boat is about to sink. We are going to drown. Don't you care?"

Jesus slowly got up and looked all around. He saw that his friends were afraid. They didn't know what do. Then He calmly said: "Shhh. Wind, be quiet. Water, be quiet." And the wind hushed. And the sea hushed. And all became quiet.

The wind and sea obeyed Jesus. The friends were amazed. Even the wind and sea did just what Jesus said.

FOR MOM AND ME

WE CAN TALK

Pretend you are in a boat rocking back and forth. The waves start getting higher and higher. You are very afraid. Call for Jesus: "Jesus, help me!" Remind your child of Jesus' words: "Shhh. Wind, be quiet. Water, be quiet." Then begin rocking very gently until you are not moving at all.

WE CAN PLAY

Provide a setting where your child can do water play. It could be a bathtub, water table, child-sized swimming pool, or a large dish pan. Supply toy boats of different sizes. Encourage your child to make waves in the water and watch the boats move up and down. Ask: "Do you think people on the boat would be afraid? In the story Jesus friends, who were big men, were afraid."

WE CAN DO

When a situation arises that frightens your child, comfort him or her. Then take the opportunity to refer back to the story, "When Jesus Said 'Shhh.'" Help your child identify why he or she is frightened. Comment: "Even grown-ups are sometimes afraid like Jesus' friends were when the storm came. But let's remember—Jesus was there."

WE CAN PRAY

"Dear God, help me remember You are there when I am afraid. Amen."

WE CAN REMEMBER

Jesus is with me when I am afraid.

JUST FOR MOM

GROW WITH YOUR CHILD

READ

Mark 4:35-41

THINK ABOUT

1. What strikes you about the setting of this passage? Journal your thoughts.

2. What was the reaction of Jesus' friends to the situation?

3. What was Jesus' reaction?

4. How does this passage speak to you about fear? Write your answer in your journal.

PRAY

Ask God to help you call on Him when you are afraid.

REMEMBER

"Who is this? Even the wind and the waves obey him!" Mark 4:41b (NIV)

CHAPTER SIXTEEN

A HOLE IN THE ROOF

"We can help our friends."
The story of the four friends, based on Mark 2:1-12

Jesus had been away on a trip. One day he came home to Capernaum. Everybody wanted to see Him. They wanted to hear Him teach about God. So Jesus began teaching. There were so many people that they could not fit into one house. Some were standing in the doorway. Others were even standing outside the door.

While Jesus was teaching, four men arrived. They were carrying their friend on a mat because he could not walk. The four men tried to get into the front door, but they could not squeeze through the crowd. What could they do? How were they going to get their friend to Jesus?

The four men decided to take their friend up to the roof. Now what? How were they going to get their friend down into the room where Jesus was? The friends began to make a hole in the roof. They worked and worked until the hole was big enough to lower their friend into the room.

When Jesus saw the man on the mat, He said: "Get up. Take your mat and walk." So the man got up, grabbed his mat, and walked away. Everyone there was watching him. All the people were amazed. They said: "We have never seen anything like this."

FOR MOM AND ME

WE CAN TALK

Stretch out on the floor, sofa, or bed with your child. Imagine that you are the "friend on the mat" and you cannot walk. Try to get up without moving your legs. Try to move from side to side. Wiggle and squirm but you still cannot get up. Then ask your child: "How do you think the man in the story felt when he could not get off his mat?"

WE CAN PLAY

Collect a cardboard box, a small doll or action figure, a string or ribbon (approximately 18 inches long), and a pair of scissors. Cut a rectangular hole in the top of the box large enough for the doll or action figure to pass through. Also cut a hole in the side of the box to use as a door. Use the cardboard rectangle for the man's mat. Place the action figure or doll on the "mat" and lower it into the box. Use Jesus' words: "Stand up, take your mat, and walk." Then have the doll or action figure walk out the door.

WE CAN DO

Think of a friend who might need help. Plan an activity with your child that would help the friend in a tangible way (such as bake cookies, weed a flower bed, water grass, feed a pet). Comment: "Remember the four men who helped their friend? We can help our friends, too."

WE CAN PRAY

"Dear God, help me be a good friend. Amen."

WE CAN REMEMBER

I can help my friends.

JUST FOR MOM

GROW WITH YOUR CHILD

READ

Mark 2:1-12

THINK ABOUT

1. What was the first dilemma in this story? Who dealt with it and how?

2. What was the second dilemma in the story? Who dealt with it and how?

3. Jesus healed the man in two ways. What were they?

4. Which do you think is more difficult and why?

PRAY

Pray for the healing you need. Write your prayer in the space provided or in your journal.

REMEMBER

When Jesus saw their faith, he said to the paralytic, "Son, your sins are forgiven." Mark 2:5 (NIV)

CHAPTER SEVENTEEN

JESUS TELLS A STORY OF A KIND MAN

"We can be kind and help others."
The story of the Good Samaritan, based on Luke 10:30-37

One day a man asked Jesus: "What does it mean to love your neighbor?" So Jesus told this story.

A man was walking down a hot, dusty road from Jerusalem to Jericho. Robbers, who were up to no good, stopped him. They beat him and left him half dead. They took everything he had, even his clothes. After awhile a priest came down the same hot, dusty road. When he saw the hurt man, he crossed to the other side and kept on walking.

Later another important man came down the same road. When he saw the hurt man lying in the dirt, he turned his head, crossed the road and kept on walking.

Then a man from Samaria came down the road. When he saw the hurt man, he stopped, got off his donkey and walked over to him. Feeling sorry for the man, the Samaritan bandaged his wounds.

Then the Samaritan put the hurt man on his donkey and led him down the road until they came to an inn. The Samaritan lifted the man off the donkey and took him inside. There he would have a good bed with a blanket and good food to eat. The next morning the man from Samaria gave the inn keeper two silver coins and said: "Take care of this man and give him everything he needs." After telling the story Jesus asked: "Who do you think was the good neighbor?"

FOR MOM AND ME

WE CAN TALK

Ask your child: "Do you remember having an 'ouchy'? What did Mommy do to make it feel better?" Then ask: "What did the man from Samaria do to help the hurt man feel better?"

WE CAN PLAY

Provide a play doctor's kit, a stuffed animal (or doll), and a box of band-aids. Give your child the opportunity to use the doctor's kit and the band-aids to care for the "hurt" animal. Allow your child to use the band-aids freely. Tell your child: "You are being kind like the man from Samaria."

WE CAN DO

Think of someone who has sustained an injury. Determine a way you and your child can be helpful to that person and his or her family. After you have completed the act of kindness, remind your child that the man from Samaria was also helpful to a person who was hurt.

WE CAN PRAY

"Dear God, help me be kind to others who need my help. Amen."

WE CAN REMEMBER

We can be kind and help others.

JUST FOR MOM

GROW WITH YOUR CHILD

READ

Luke 10:30-37

THINK ABOUT

1. What is the obvious problem in this story?

2. Why do you think the first two men passed by on the other side without offering help to the man who was hurt?

3. What do you think motivated the Samaritan to help the man who was hurt? Why do you think Jesus referred to the Samaritan man as a "neighbor?"

4. Who is your neighbor?

PRAY

Ask God to help you become more of a "neighbor" to those around you.

REMEMBER

[Jesus said] "Which of these three do you think was a neighbor to the man who fell into the hands of robbers?" Luke 10:36 (NIV)

CHAPTER EIGHTEEN

REMEMBERING TO SAY "THANK YOU"

"It is important to say thank you."
The story of the Ten Lepers, based on Luke 17:11-18

Jesus was traveling with His friends to Jerusalem. He went to a village where there were ten men who had a bad skin disease. Their bodies were covered with sores. The men stood far away from Jesus because they were afraid He would catch the skin disease. The men called out in a loud voice: "Jesus, help us!"

When Jesus saw them, He told them to go and show themselves to the leaders at the temple (church). While they were on their way to the temple, all their sores disappeared. They were all better.

One of the men, seeing that the sores were all gone, wanted to tell Jesus "thank you." He went back to look for Jesus. When he found Him, he fell facedown at His feet and shouted: "Thank You! Thank You!"

Jesus asked: "Where are the other nine men? Aren't their sores better? Didn't they want to thank Me as well?" Jesus told the man to get up and go on his way. Jesus was glad the one man remembered to say: "Thank you."

FOR MOM AND ME

WE CAN TALK

Ask your child: "What would you like to thank God for?" Then share with your child something for which you would like to thank God. Take a moment to thank God for the things mentioned.

WE CAN PLAY

On a large sheet of paper or poster board, write "Thank You, God, for . . ." across the top. Then number to five down the left margin. As your child tells you five things for which he or she is thankful, write them beside the respective numbers. Let your child decorate the poster with colorful stickers.

WE CAN DO

Gather a transparent container and an assortment of buttons (marbles, dried beans, or something similar). Whenever anyone in the family remembers to say "thank you," he or she can drop a button in the container. When the container is filled, the family gets to enjoy a predetermined "treat" such as ice cream cones, movie night at home with popcorn, or going to a favorite restaurant.

WE CAN PRAY

"Dear God, teach me to say 'thank you.' Amen."

WE CAN REMEMBER

I can say "thank you."

JUST FOR MOM

GROW WITH YOUR CHILD

READ

Luke 17:11-18

THINK ABOUT

1. Why did the men need Jesus' help?

2. How did Jesus respond to the men?

3. Why do you think only one man came back to thank Jesus?

4. Do you identify more with the man who returned to say "thank you" or the nine who did not? Why?

PRAY

Pray about becoming more grateful and expressing your gratitude to God.

REMEMBER

Jesus asked, "Were not all ten cleansed? Where are the other nine?" Luke 17:17 (NIV)

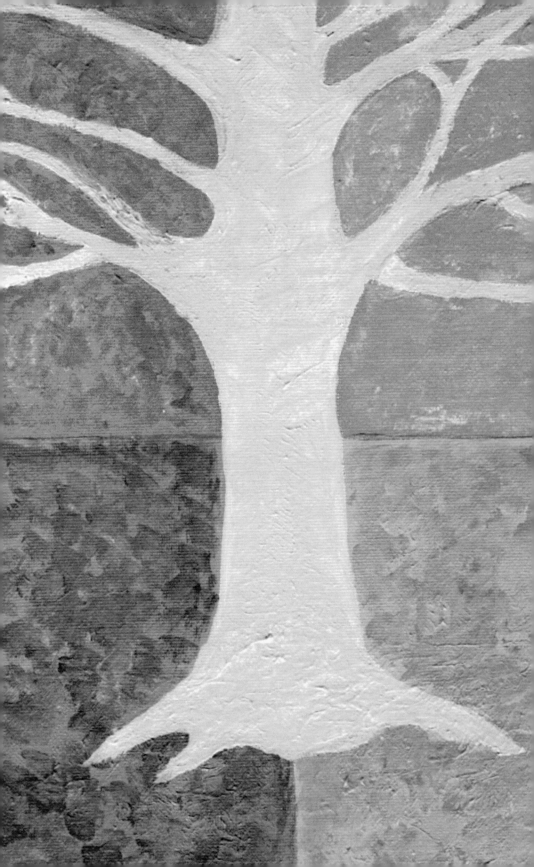

CHAPTER NINETEEN

NO FRIENDS

"Jesus knows your name and loves you."
The story of Zacchaeus, based on Luke 19:1-9

One day Jesus was traveling through the town of Jericho. A man named Zacchaeus lived there. He was very rich. Sometimes he took things from other people that did not belong to him.

Zacchaeus heard Jesus was in Jericho and wanted to see Him. But Zacchaeus was a short man. He knew he could never see over the crowd. Most of the people were taller than Zacchaeus. So what was he to do? How was he going to see Jesus? He decided he would climb a sycamore tree.

Jesus came along, stopped under the tree, and looked up at Zacchaeus. Jesus called to him: "Zacchaeus, come down quickly. I want to go to your house today." Zacchaeus came down out of the tree. He was happy to have Jesus go to his house.

After spending the day with Jesus, Zacchaeus decided he wouldn't take things that didn't belong to him anymore. But more than anything, Zacchaeus was glad Jesus knew his name and loved him and wanted to be his friend.

FOR MOM AND ME

WE CAN TALK

Use hand motions to pretend to:

Climb up a tree

Look for Jesus

Hear His voice

Motion for Zacchaeus

Climb down from the tree

WE CAN PLAY

Pretend Jesus comes to spend the day at your house. Provide some toy dishes and encourage your child to make and serve a special meal for Jesus. Ask your child: "What would you serve Jesus to eat if He came to our house?"

WE CAN DO

Talk with your child about names. Ask your child what his or her name is. Then ask: "Do you know mommy's name (Jennifer, Kate)? Do you know daddy's name (Chris, Tom)?" Then suggest that your child name as many friends as he or she can. Comment: "Jesus knows all our names and loves us all."

WE CAN PRAY

"Dear God, thank You that Jesus knows my name and loves me. Amen."

WE CAN REMEMBER

Jesus knows my name and loves me.

JUST FOR MOM

GROW WITH YOUR CHILD

READ

Luke 19:1-9

THINK ABOUT

1. How do you think Zacchaeus felt when Jesus called him by name? Wanted to go home with him?

2. What did Zacchaeus choose to do as a result of being with Jesus?

3. How does it affect you when you hear that Jesus knows your name? What if you heard that Jesus wanted to come to your home, how would it affect you?

4. Spending time with Jesus changed Zacchaeus' life? How might spending time with Jesus change your life?

PRAY

Thank God for loving you and wanting to spend time with you.

REMEMBER

"Zacchaeus, come down immediately. I must stay at your house today."
Luke 19:5b (NIV)

CHAPTER TWENTY

TIME FOR LITTLE CHILDREN

"Children are special to Jesus."
The story of Jesus and the children, based on Matthew 19:1-2, 13-15

One day Jesus was teaching in Judea, just across the Jordan River. Many people, mostly grown-ups, gathered to hear Him. Jesus was teaching them very important things about God.

Mamas and daddies brought their children, even their little babies, to the place where Jesus was teaching. They wanted their children to be close to Jesus. But Jesus' helpers thought He was too busy teaching important things. They said: "Move along. Jesus is teaching. He doesn't have time for the children." Then Jesus' helpers tried to shoo the children away.

When Jesus saw that His helpers were sending the children away, He was not happy. He wanted the children to come close. Jesus wanted to pray for the children. He said: "Let the children come to me. Don't keep them away."

Then Jesus gathered the children, even the little babies, in His arms and prayed for them. Jesus loved the children. They were important to Him.

FOR MOM AND ME

WE CAN TALK

Cuddle your child in your lap. Pray a simple prayer asking God to bless him or her, just like Jesus did.

WE CAN PLAY

Let your child choose five of his or her stuffed animals. Play a game of "Shoo Away." One by one your child will "shoo" each of the animals away. He or she may actually take the animals to another area of the room. At the end of the game, encourage your child to gather the animals and hold them close. Remind your child that Jesus gathered the children and held them close.

WE CAN DO

Plan a "You Are Special Party" with your child. Invite two of your child's friends along with their moms. Gather construction paper, sequins, buttons, ribbon, lace, stickers, glue, and child-sized scissors. Make "You Are Special" cards for each other. Exchange cards with a guest. Serve lemonade and cookies. Say: "You are special. I love you."

WE CAN PRAY

"Dear God, thank You that I am special to Jesus. Amen."

WE CAN REMEMBER

I am special to Jesus.

JUST FOR MOM

GROW WITH YOUR CHILD

READ

Matthew 19:1-2, 13-15

THINK ABOUT

1. What was Jesus doing at beginning of this story?

2. What did the parents want from Jesus?

3. What was Jesus' response?

4. What do you want Jesus to do for your child(ren)?

PRAY

Pray asking God for His blessing on your child(ren).

REMEMBER

Jesus said: "Let the little children come to me . . ." Matthew 19:14a (NIV)

CHAPTER TWENTY-ONE

A LITTLE LUNCH FOR A BIG CROWD

"We can share what we have."
A boy shares his lunch, based on John 6:1-13

Jesus was in a boat crossing the Sea of Galilee. When He got to the other side, a large crowd of people met Him there. Jesus welcomed the people and told them about God.

Late in the afternoon, Jesus' helpers came to Him and said: "We must send the people away. The people are getting hungry and there is nothing to eat." Jesus said: "We can't send them away. We need to give them something to eat."

Andrew, Peter's brother, said: "There is a boy here who has five small loaves of barley bread and two fish. But what good is that with so many hungry people?"

Jesus told his helpers to have the people sit down on the grass. The boy shared his lunch with Jesus. Then Jesus took the five small barley loaves in His hands, gave thanks to God, and passed the bread to the people.

Then He took the two fish in His hands, gave thanks to God, and passed the fish to the people. After everyone had plenty to eat, Jesus' helpers gathered up the food that was left over so nothing would be wasted. The food leftover filled twelve large baskets.

FOR MOM AND ME

WE CAN TALK

Ask your child: "If you could share something with Jesus, what would it be?" Then tell your child what you would share with Jesus if you could.

WE CAN PLAY

Cut or tear brown construction paper into five circles that represent five loaves of bread. Out of blue construction paper cut two fish shapes. Provide a small basket. Encourage your child to count the loaves and put them in the basket. Then ask your child to count the fish and put them in the basket. Remind your child of the boy who shared his five loaves and two fish.

WE CAN DO

Buy frozen bread dough and bake the bread with your child. (Consider baking a loaf for a neighbor also.) Cut it and serve it to your family. As you enjoy the bread together, retell the story "A Boy Shares His Lunch."

WE CAN PRAY

"Dear God, thank You that we can share. Amen."

WE CAN REMEMBER

I can share what I have.

JUST FOR MOM

GROW WITH YOUR CHILD

READ

John 6:1-13

THINK ABOUT

1. How many people were in the crowd that day?

2. How much food was available to feed the crowd? What dilemma did these facts pose?

3. What was the disciples' response? What was Jesus' response?

4. When faced with an impossible situation, what do you do?

PRAY

Ask God to help you understand there is no situation too impossible for Him.

REMEMBER

So they gathered them and filled twelve baskets with the pieces of the five barley loaves left over by those who had eaten. John 6:13 (NIV)

CHAPTER TWENTY-TWO

ONE SUNDAY MORNING

"Jesus is alive!"
The story of the empty tomb, based on Matthew 28:1-10

On Friday afternoon Jesus died on the cross. But early Sunday morning, just as the sun began to shine, Mary Magdalene and the other women came to the tomb. This was the tomb where Jesus' body had been placed.

The women took jars of spices and bottles of perfume. Just as they neared the tomb, the earth began to shake and rock under their feet. Mary Magdalene and the other women were afraid, very afraid.

Then God's angel came down from heaven and appeared just where the women were standing. The angel took hold of the big stone and began to roll it away from the door of the tomb.

The angel said: "Don't be afraid. I know you're looking for Jesus, but He is not here. He is alive! Come look into the tomb and you'll see that it is empty." Then the angel told the women to go quickly and talk to Jesus' disciples. Tell them He is alive and He will meet them in Galilee.

FOR MOM AND ME

WE CAN TALK

Say to your child: "Let's pretend to roll a big, heavy stone." Then say: "In the story we read that the angel rolled the big stone away from the tomb." Then ask your child: "Do you remember what the angel said? Let's say the words together: 'Jesus is not here. He is alive!'"

WE CAN PLAY

Place an assortment of spices such as cinnamon, rosemary, and curry on a tray. Add some of your favorite fragrances such as perfume, body lotion, and shower gel. Cotton balls are good for this. Allow your child to smell and identity the different spices and fragrances. Refer back to the story where the women brought spices and perfumes to the tomb.

WE CAN DO

Help your child act out the story "He Is Risen" for the family. Drape a blanket over a table so the edges touch the floor to serve as the tomb.

Characters: One angel and one or more women.
The women rush to the tomb and say: "Where is Jesus?"
The angel pops out from under the table and says: "He is not here!"
The women say: "Where is He?"
The angel says: "He is not here. He is alive!"

WE CAN PRAY

"Thank You, God, that Jesus is alive. Amen."

WE CAN REMEMBER

Jesus is alive!

JUST FOR MOM

GROW WITH YOUR CHILD

READ

Matthew 28:1-10

THINK ABOUT

1. Where were the women going on that early Sunday morning? Why?

2. What did they find when they arrived at the tomb?

3. What was significant about the message they received from the angel?

4. What is the significance of this message for you? Journal your thoughts and feelings.

PRAY

Ask God to help you allow Jesus to be more "alive" in your heart.

REMEMBER

. . . they came to him, clasped his feet and worshiped him.
Matthew 28:9b (NIV)

CHAPTER TWENTY-THREE

BREAKFAST ON THE BEACH

"Jesus loved and served his friends."
The story of breakfast with Jesus, based on John 21:1-14

One evening Peter decided to go fishing in the Sea of Galilee. His friends, James and John, went with him. They fished and fished and fished. All night they fished. But they did not catch a single one.

Early in the morning, Peter, James, and John saw Jesus standing on the beach. He called out: "Have you caught anything for breakfast?" "No," they answered.

Then Jesus said: "Throw out your net on the other side of the boat." When they did what Jesus said, their net was so full of fish they could hardly pull it in. They pulled and pulled and pulled until they finally got the net into the boat. They were surprised that the net did not break. The Bible says there were 153 fish.

After they pulled the heavy net full of fish into the boat, Peter was so excited he jumped in the water and swam to the shore. The other friends followed in the boat.

As they neared the shore they could smell fish cooking. They could see a small fire burning. Jesus was cooking for them. Jesus said: "Come, and have breakfast." Then Jesus served his friends fish and bread.

FOR MOM AND ME

WE CAN TALK

After telling the story, snuggle with your child. Tell him or her: "I love you. I want to take care of you just like Jesus cared for His friends."

WE CAN PLAY

Crumple orange tissue paper to look like a camp fire. Provide play dishes and plastic toy fish (or fish cut from construction paper). Encourage your child to cook the fish on the fire and share it with you. Ask: "Remember when Jesus cooked fish for his friends?" Then add: "He loved his friends and enjoyed cooking breakfast for them."

WE CAN DO

Reinforce the concept of the story. Make cookies together and deliver them to someone you love. Remind your child that Jesus cared for and served those He loved.

WE CAN PRAY

"Dear God, thank You for teaching me how to love and serve others. Amen."

WE CAN REMEMBER

I can love and serve others.

JUST FOR MOM

GROW WITH YOUR CHILD

READ

John 21:1-14

THINK ABOUT

1. Do you think Peter, James, and John were frustrated? Why?

2. How did Jesus remedy their struggle? What happened when they followed Jesus' instructions?

3. How did Jesus show His love and care for them?

4. How does Jesus' model of servanthood speak to you today? Does it challenge you? Why or why not?

PRAY

Ask God to show you the true meaning of servanthood.

REMEMBER

Jesus said to them, "Come and have breakfast." John 21:12a (NIV)

CHAPTER TWENTY-FOUR

WHO'S KNOCKING?

"Friends pray for each other."
The story of Peter's praying friends, based on Acts 12:1-19

Peter was in jail and could not get out. Peter's friends were back home praying for him. They were praying very hard.

One night an angel appeared to Peter while he was asleep. The angel told Peter: "Wake up. You've got to get out of here." Then the angel said: "Put on your clothes, put on your sandals, put on your coat, and follow me." So Peter put on his clothes, put on his sandals, put on his coat, and followed the angel out of the jail.

Peter walked down the street until he came to the house where his friends were praying. He knocked on the door. Knock, knock, knock. His friends didn't hear him because they were still praying. Rhoda, a servant girl, came to the door. When she recognized Peter's voice, she was so excited that she forgot to open it. She ran inside and said: "Peter's at the door!"

The friends did not believe her. They thought she was crazy. Peter kept knocking. Knock, knock, knock. When the friends finally heard him and opened the door, they were amazed. Peter motioned for the friends to be quiet. Shhh. Then he told his friends how he had gotten out of jail. He was glad to have such good friends to pray for him.

FOR MOM AND ME

WE CAN TALK

Help your child think of a friend the two of you can pray for. Then in simple words, pray for the friend.

WE CAN PLAY

Act out the story of Peter knocking at the door.

Peter: (Knocks at the door.)

Rhoda: "I hear someone knocking at the door." (Goes to the door.) "Who's there?"

Peter: "It's me, Peter."

Rhoda: "Oh my, it's Peter." (Runs to tell the praying friends.) "Stop praying everybody. Peter's at the door."

Peter: (Knocks at the door.)

Rhoda: (Opens the door.)

Peter: (Peter comes in.) "Shhh, be quiet."

Peter: (Make the sound of Peter running to his friends.) "Look, here I am! Thank you for praying for me."

WE CAN DO

Choose a friend to whom you want to send a card. Provide paper and Do-A-Dots. Say something like: "I'm glad you're my friend and I'm praying for you." Mail the card.

WE CAN PRAY

"Dear God, help my friend (name), _____. Amen."

WE CAN REMEMBER

I can pray for my friends.

JUST FOR MOM

GROW WITH YOUR CHILD

READ

Acts 12:1-19

THINK ABOUT

1. Why was Peter in jail?

2. What was miraculous about Peter's escape?

3. Why do you think Peter's friends were praying for him?

4. What do you think they were praying? What do you think it means to earnestly pray?

PRAY

Pray for the perseverance and courage to keep on praying.

REMEMBER

So Peter was kept in prison, but the church was earnestly praying to God for him. Acts 12:5 (NIV)

CHAPTER TWENTY-FIVE

GATHERING TO PRAY

"It is important to gather together to pray and to learn about God."
The story of Lydia, based on Acts 16:11-15

P aul and Barnabas had been traveling around the hot, dusty countryside. One day they traveled to the city of Philippi. They decided to stay there for several days.

On the Sabbath (Sunday) they left the city. They walked outside the city gate and down to the river. As they walked along the river, they heard people praying. They found a group of women and sat down with them to talk. It was a shady, cool place to gather.

One of the women was named Lydia. Her business was selling purple cloth. Lydia knew about God but she wanted to learn more. She listened very carefully as Paul and Barnabas taught about God.

When they finished teaching, Lydia knew more about God and loved Him even more. She was grateful that Paul and Barnabas had come. So she invited the men to stay at her house.

Paul and Barnabas looked at each other. They were not sure about going to Lydia's house to stay. But Lydia asked them again to come to her house. So they went. Lydia was glad because she could continue to talk, to pray, and to learn more about God.

FOR MOM AND ME

WE CAN TALK

As you snuggle with your child, ask: "Who tells you about God?" Give your child time to respond. Then ask: "Who prays for you?"

WE CAN PLAY

Set up a pretend store where your child can sell purple items. Gather as many as you can find. Let your child make price tags. Pretend to buy and sell the purple items. Remind your child that in the story Lydia sold purple cloth.

WE CAN DO

Attend church as a family. After church talk about how Lydia and her friends gathered together to pray and learn about God.

WE CAN PRAY

"Dear God, thank You we can go to church to pray and learn about You. Amen."

WE CAN REMEMBER

I can pray and learn about God.

JUST FOR MOM

GROW WITH YOUR CHILD

READ

Acts 16:11-15

THINK ABOUT

1. Why did Paul and Barnabas go down by the river?

2. Who did they find down by the river?

3. What was Lydia's response to Paul and Barnabas' teaching?

4. Compare yourself to Lydia. Write your observations in your journal.

PRAY

Ask God for a more teachable heart.

REMEMBER

The Lord opened her heart to respond to Paul's message.
Acts 16:14b (NIV)

FACILITATOR'S GUIDE

AN EXPLANATION

This guide is designed to help you facilitate a small group study (eight to ten is a good number) using content from Remember, and Don't Forget. Participants in your group will be moms (or grand moms) of children between the ages of two and eight.

Since there are twenty-five Bible stories with related activities and Scripture reflection, the question may surface: "How can we use this material in a short-term study?" Obviously you will not want to include all twenty-five stories in a small group study.

Before you pull together your small group, determine the number of sessions to include in your study. Keep in mind that there will be an introductory session and a closing session. Each session is developed within a 90-minute timeframe.

A RECOMMENDATION

The number of sessions may vary with your group, but the level of commitment will remain stronger with a fewer number of sessions. We recommend that your study include seven sessions:
- an introductory session
- five Bible story-related sessions (Choose any five stories from the twenty-five stories in *Remember, and Don't Forget.*)
- a closing session

THE GOALS

The goals of this study are:
- to establish a pattern of teaching Bible truths to children while

building a routine of devotional time for Mom

-to get the Scripture story into the head and heart of the moms

- to get the Scripture story into the head and heart of their child(ren)

-to teach moms how to interact with their children in age-appropriate ways

-to teach moms and children how to pray individually and together

-to encourage a deeper and more authentic relationship with Christ for both mom and child

A REMINDER

The essential element of this study is prayer. Pray for your participants and your time together in small group.

WEEK ONE
INTRODUCTORY SESSION

BEFORE THE SESSION

1. Determine the time and location of the study.

2. Communicate the following information to the participants:
    -Encourage them to bring a Bible to each session. (Have Bibles available for those who may not have one or who forget to bring theirs.)
    -Remind them to download their copy of the book, *Remember, and Don't Forget*, and bring it to each session.

3. Plan to provide refreshments for the introductory session.

4. Determine if and how childcare will be provided.

5. Be prepared to share information about the authors, the components of the study, and the session format at this meeting.

6. Pray for the moms who will attend this study. Also pray for their children.

DURING THE SESSION
1. Arrange chairs in a circle.

2. Greet each participant and provide a nametag.

3. Invite each participant to enjoy the refreshments and then to find a seat in the circle.

4. Ask participants to introduce themselves by sharing the following information:
   - Name
   - Children's names and ages
   - Favorite hobby

5. Make a list of participants' names, telephone numbers (including cell numbers), home addresses, and e-mail addresses.

6. Emphasize meeting times and location as well as the necessary weekly preparation.

7. Discuss any issues dealing with childcare (logistical elements such as ages, cost, etc.).

8. Introduce the book, *Remember, and Don't Forget,* and share information about the authors and the components and format of the study.

9. Assign the story for the week and give instructions regarding the assignment. Each assignment includes:
- Reading the story to your child
- Participating in the "For Mom and Me" activities with your child
- Completing the "Just for Mom" section

10. Close the session with prayer.

AFTER THE SESSION
1. Pray for the moms to follow through with their assignment.

2. Pray for the moms as they interact with the Scripture.

3. Communicate words of encouragement to the moms during the week.

WEEKS TWO THROUGH SIX
FIVE BIBLE STORY-RELATED SESSIONS

BEFORE THE SESSION
1. Review the Bible story for the week.

2. Review the "For Mom and Me" activities.

3. Complete the "Just for Mom" section.

DURING THE SESSION
Greet and Open with Prayer (5 minutes)

Encourage Community (15 minutes)
Encourage community by asking one of these connection questions

each week:

1. What was the highlight of your week?

2. Share one humorous moment you experienced with your child this past week.

3. What one word from the lesson stood out to you and why?

Engage with the Bible Story (30 minutes)

1. Read this week's Bible story aloud.

2. Answer the following questions:
    - How did your child respond to the story?
    - What caught his/her attention? Why?
    - What Biblical truth surfaced as you read and discussed the story?
    - How did your child respond to the activities?
    - Was there one particular activity that he/she desired to repeat?
    - What Biblical truth surfaced as you worked through the activities?

Engage with the Scripture Passage (30 minutes)

1. Ask all participants to look at the "Just for Mom" section related to this week's Bible story.

2. Then read the Scripture passage aloud.

3. Read aloud each question under "Think About" and discuss.

Close the Session (10 minutes)

1. Give participants a few moments to pray silently the prayer at the end of the "Just for Mom" section.

2. Read together aloud the "Remember" verse.

WEEK SEVEN
CLOSING SESSION

BEFORE THE SESSION

1. Contact each participant and ask her to:
   - Bring her favorite snack food to share with the group.
   - Come prepared to share her favorite Bible story and tell why.

2. Pray for the moms and their children.

DURING THE SESSION

1. Greet the moms as they arrive.

2. Enjoy the food and fellowship. Ask participants to tell why their snack food is their favorite.

3. Ask each mom to share her favorite Bible story and why.

4. Ask each mom to share her favorite activity with her child and why.

5. Ask each mom to share one thing she learned from a favorite "Just for Mom" section.

6. Read aloud Deuteronomy 8:1-11. Discuss the following:
   - Why did Moses encourage the people of God to carefully follow God's commands? (See v. 1.)
   - What is "the land" that God is promising to us today? How do we get there? (Read John 3:16 aloud as a group).
   - In the Bible stories and Scripture passages that you have read during this study, what are some of your highlights and take-aways? Why?
   - Read aloud Deut. 31:8. According to this Scripture passage, who is going to help you "remember and not forget"?

CLOSE THE SESSION

Pray thanking God for giving us His Word and helping us teach our children to "remember and not forget".

NOTE:

Consider providing other studies based on *Remember, and Don't Forget* using a different set of stories but the same format provided in this Facilitator's Guide.